Japanese knotweed, also known as Fallopia japonica, Polygonum cuspidatum and Reynoutria japonica

JAPANESE KNOTWEED

UNEARTHING THE TRUTH

NICOLAS SEAL

The underground rhizome
and root system

UNEARTHING THE TRUTH

How a Valuable Plant from the East became the Root of Evil in the West

---

Nicolas Seal

Illustrations Lizzie Harper

Photography Justin Creedy-Smith
and others

First published in 2018

First edition

Carrowmore.ie

British Library Cataloguing in Publication Data.

A catalogue record for this book is available from the British Library.

ISBN: 978-1-9999915-1-7

Japanese knotweed, a plant with more
photosynthetic material per sqm than
nearly all other plants

PREFACE

I'm frequently amazed at some of the myths I read in the press and on the internet about Japanese knotweed. With over 20 years' experience specialising in its control and eradication, it's clear to me that Japanese knotweed gets its fair share of inaccurate reporting. Perhaps it's not surprising therefore that one sees a massive range of reactions from those affected, from murder and suicide at one extreme end of the spectrum, to "it's only a weed, what's the problem?" at the other.

High time, I thought, to set the record straight, so you can decide if Japanese knotweed deserves its fierce reputation.

I'd like to thank Trevor Renals from the UK Environment Agency, for his direction, expertise and support over the years. Also, I'd like to thank Richard Shaw and the Centre for Agriculture and Biosciences International (CABI) for their contributions to research, and for permission to include some of their photographs in this book.

I extend my thanks to Carla Teune from Hortus Botanicus in Leiden for her unparalleled knowledge of Philipp von Siebold. Also, to his descendent Diana Seabold, thought to be his first cousin fourth removed who gave me a fascinating insight into the man. His life story is summarized in the book *"Siebold and Japan - his life and work"*.

Thanks to my colleagues at Environet for their support and photographs; to Jeremy and Fiona for their editorial input, to Justin and Lizzie for bringing the book alive with their photographs and illustrations, and to Ella for her design input. And lastly to my wife Bertie for her encouragement, enthusiasm, support and input.

Next page: Japanese knotweed - indisputably the UK's most aggressive and destructive plant

INTRODUCTION

No other plant is more notorious than Japanese knotweed (Fallopia japonica), the cause amongst other things, of neighbourly vendettas, court cases and even murder and suicide. Although it has been described as "indisputably the UK's most aggressive and destructive plant" and a "triffid like super-weed", there is another more agreeable side to the Japanese knotweed story.

It has been used in Chinese medicine for its remarkable biological attributes for hundreds of years. There was even a time when our much maligned Fallopia japonica was as popular with horticulturalists and gardeners as Spiraea and Fatsia are today. Incidentally, all these plants share japonica in their Latin name. Japanese knotweed has had many admirers and even won the gold medal from the Society of Agriculture and Horticulture at Utrecht in 1847 described as "the most interesting new ornamental plant of the year".

Despite its fearsome reputation it's worth remembering that Japanese knotweed is only a weed when it's found growing in the wrong place. In other situations, it might not only prove harmless and beautiful, but might even have a future value.

My journey will take you back to its origins in Japan, explain its history, how to identify it, describe its anatomy and physiology, and suggest why it has spread so successfully. I'll conclude with some possible and surprisingly beneficial uses for the plant. This book is written the root of evil to decide whether Japanese knotweed is truly your foe and will be of particular interest if you have it growing on your property or that of your neighbours.

HISTORY AND EVOLUTION

Japanese knotweed is a herbaceous perennial flowering shrub from the buckwheat family, Polygonaceae.

It is thought to have originated approximately 125 million years ago on Mount Fuji in Japan, an active volcano extremely hostile to plant life. Japanese knotweed proved itself to be an early coloniser, with the rare ability to survive up to 2,400m above sea level.

It took root in other parts of Japan, Taiwan, Korea and China, areas considered to be its native environment today. These countries have a temperate climate with relatively high rainfall and moderate temperature variations both seasonally and daily.

The plant has evolved characteristics that helped it succeed beyond its natural environment. Hybrid varieties of knotweed have developed by cross-fertilisation of closely related species, such as Giant knotweed, to form Bohemian knotweed.

Over the last 150 years knotweed has spread at an exponential rate in Canada, USA, Australia, New Zealand, Europe and especially the UK. Is this down to its evolutionary success, interference by man, or perhaps both?

Approx 500 million years	292 million years	130-140 million years	2,000 years	Nearly 200 years ago
Earliest land-plants	Dinosaurs	Flowering plants	Christ	Japanese knotweed import to Europe

THE EXOTIC PLANT HUNTERS

In the early 19th century European adventurers with botanical interests went in search of exotic plants to bring back home to cultivate. Hundreds of species found new homes at the Royal Botanic Gardens in Kew, London, and other nurseries and gardens throughout Europe, North America and Australasia. Horticulture became a big business.

Some of these species could not survive in these new habitats, however, many grew in harmony with neighbouring plants and a select few found the conditions perfect. With no predators, they quickly established themselves, displacing all native flora that dared compete with them for light and water.

Some notable examples are Kudzu in the United States, Floating pennywort, Himalayan balsam, and of course Japanese knotweed and its hybrid varieties.

Above: Copyright CABI 2018. What looks like a well tended flat lawn is actually a pond infested with Azolla

Right: Copyright CABI 2018. Close up of Azolla

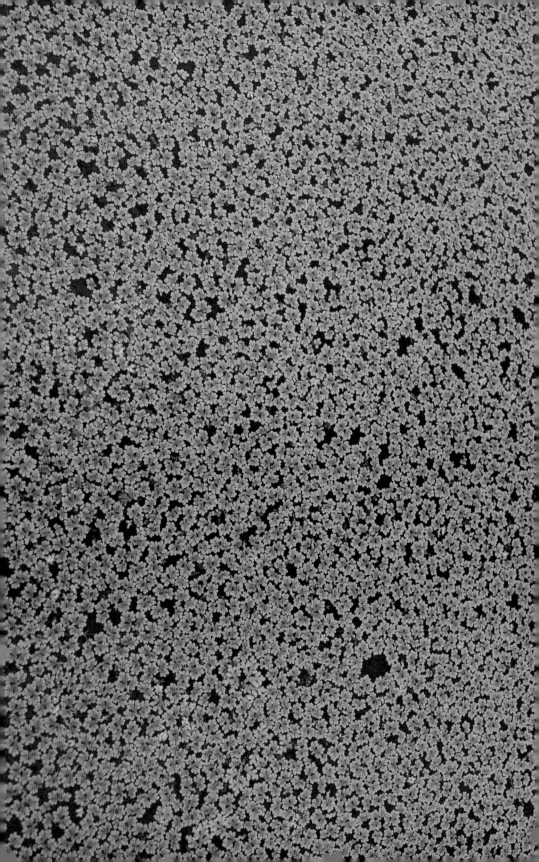

Left: Copyright CABI 2018. Pretty pink flowers of Himalayan balsam, a plant spread by seed and often found along watercourses

Above: Copyright CABI 2018. Gunnera tinctoria, otherwise known as giant rhubarb

Next page: Copyright CABI 2018. Ludwigia, an aquatic plant infesting a large area in France

PHILIPP FRANZ VON SIEBOLD (1796-1866)

The Bavarian physician Philipp Franz von Siebold is generally credited – or blamed – for the import of Japanese knotweed to Europe and beyond.

Siebold was an intelligent, well-educated but arrogant man with wide ranging interests in medicine and natural history who collected thousands of plant and animal species from Japan. While he is credited with introducing well-known, decorative and much loved Japanese plants such as wisteria, hydrangea, hosta, camellia, mulberry and peony-rose, he has become increasingly castigated for importing Japanese knotweed to Europe in the 1840s.

Sculpture of Philipp Franz von Siebold in the garden of Sieboldhuis, Rapenburg, Leiden

With help from his eminent physician grandfather, Karl Kaspar von Siebold, he secured the post of Surgeon-General in the Dutch East Indies. After only a few months he was sent to the Dutch Trading Post on Deshima, a 2.2 acre artificial island on the Nagasaki River in Japan, arriving in 1823. He was subsequently expelled for alleged espionage in 1829 when he obtained several detailed maps of Japan and Korea, an act strictly forbidden by the Japanese government.

During and after this period Siebold's botanical collections were shipped back to Europe, many of which can be seen in his former house at Rapenburg 19, now the Japanese Museum called "SieboldHuis", in the beautiful Dutch city of Leiden.

Siebold lived at Rapenburg 19 from 1832 to 1838. The house is a few doors along from Leiden University's botanical gardens "Hortus Botanicus", which he provided with many plant specimens, some of which exist to this day. In 1840 he bought land in the village of Leiderdorp, now part of Leiden, where he built "Nippon", his new home, and his commercial nursery Von Siebold & Company of Leiden. This had nearly a thousand different plant species and varieties at the time of his death, aged 70, in 1866.

The Japanese Musuem "Sieboldhuis", Siebold's home from 1832-38 and now housing some of his collection of Japanese artefacts, plant and animal specimens

In 1850 Siebold sent a sample of Japanese knotweed to the Royal Botanic Gardens in Kew, London. With accolades and awards, notably the gold medal in 1847, its commercial propagation was assured.

Nurserymen were quick to find it very easy to cultivate, and to exploit the commercial benefits of this newly fashionable ornamental plant.

It's possible that an earlier sample was sent to London possibly by Siebold in 1825. Records exist of a plant named "Reynoutria japonica" growing in an artificial swamp at the Horticultural Society's garden in Chiswick, which was subsequently identified as Japanese knotweed.

Whatever the truth, Siebold's story is inextricably entwined, for better or worse, with that of the plant he did so much to popularise.

Café Decima, on Decimastraat, Leiden, built on Siebold's former nursery site Nippon. Decimastraat is named after Deshima Island, the trading post on the Nagasaki River, Japan where Siebold lived from 1823 to 1829

I felt compelled to continue my research, so in 2017 I visited Leiden to see if it was indeed the distribution hub for Japanese knotweed. A visit to "Hortus Botanicus", confirmed the presence of knotweed. One mature shrub stands proud, contained by constant pulling and cutting, preserved rather unnecessarily in the memory of Siebold.

It's highly probable that this long-lived plant has grown from a rhizome specimen given to the botanical garden by Siebold in 1830-1840, and due to its regenerative powers is likely to out-survive me, perhaps my children, and possibly my future grandchildren.

Three other areas of knotweed can be found within these botanical gardens, despite repeated efforts to banish the plant. Mature knotweed can also be found just outside the Botanical Gardens and Leiden University, growing up through the road and into adjoining gardens. A trip along the canals revealed numerous large stands of knotweed growing on the banks.

A specimen of Japanese knotweed in "Hortus Botanicus, Leiden", thought to have been donated by Siebold, and possibly one of the first knotweed plants to have grown outside of its native habitat

I also visited Siebold's former nursery site in Leiderdorp which was demolished in 1930 to create housing along two streets now named in his memory - Sieboldstraat and Decimastraat.

When two British horticulturalists, Messrs F.W. Burbidge and P. Barr, visited the site in 1883 they found it derelict, describing it as a jungle overrun by one plant - Japanese knotweed.

I found mature Japanese knotweed some 10m away close to the road junction of Lage Rijndijk and Sieboldstrasse, but not on the former nursery site.

Either the British nurserymen misidentified the invasive plant, or it goes to prove that it is possible to eradicate it. Perhaps the knotweed on Lage Rijndijk is the piece that got away!

Left: Mature knotweed growing through a cobbled street close to Hortus Botanicus and Leiden University

Next page: Looking down the canal towards Leiden University, Rapenburg, Leiden

HOW IT SPREAD THROUGHOUT THE UK

It is debatable whether Philipp Von Siebold and his contemporary plantsmen should be solely blamed for the plant's introduction to the UK.

Another, perhaps unintended means of spreading, may be found in the lack of any bio-security in shipping and trading practices in the 19th and 20th centuries, and might help to explain why the earliest sightings of knotweed were close to the main ports.

Ships bound for other parts of the world would sometimes return to the UK without a return cargo. To improve stability, ballast was loaded onto the empty ship, often in the form of soil from the last port of departure.

Upon arrival back at a UK port, the ballast was dumped to make way for the next cargo. The theory goes that ships loading ballast contaminated with Japanese knotweed rhizomes would have provided the perfect conduit for the spread of the plant to the main trading nations of the time.

Ballast Island off Portmadog in North Wales is a small man-made island of ballast spoil dumped by returning ships involved in the Welsh slate trade. Now it provides botanists with a rich floral bank of plant and seed specimens from around the world. Japanese knotweed is known to be present in Porthmadog and surrounding areas, providing circumstantial evidence to support this theory. Comparing the genetic code of knotweed across the country with the sample in Hortus Botanicus in Leiden might dispel this theory – perhaps a worthy PHD research project for any budding scientist.

The spread of Japanese knotweed throughout the last few decades has been exponential. It is thought to affect up to 1 in 20 residential properties in the UK. In addition to gardens, it is found growing along railway lines, road verges, on riverbanks, canals, brownfield sites, commercial and industrial property and in woodland. Even graveyards are not immune to its relentless invasion. It grows in any type of soil, even from rocky outcrops.

Right: Japanese knotweed damaginga concrete culvert in Wales

Next page: Japanese knotweed growing from a rocky outcrop

A large infestation of Japanese knotweed along a railway in the UK, having a significant impact on neighbouring residential properties

Previous page: A neglected graveyard in Wales, infested with Japanese knotweed

Left: Japanese knotweed growing along a road in Surrey, England

Right: Japanese knotweed growing along a canal in Leiden, Netherlands

THE REALISATION – THE GOOD, THE BAD, AND THE UGLY

Japanese knotweed was promoted and sold as an ornamental plant from around 1850. In 1981 the Wildlife and Countryside Act made it illegal to cause or allow it to spread into the wild. It was included in many of Gertrude Jekyll's garden and landscape designs in the early 20th century.

However, its virtues began to be questioned at the end of the 19th century, notably by the horticulturalist Walters in 1887 in his account of the flora of Alexandra Park in Oldham, Lancashire, where he noted that Japanese knotweed *"turns up unexpectedly in nearly every piece of cultivated ground"*. By the 1930s Japanese knotweed was known in East Cornwall as "Hancock's Curse", possibly linked to Hancock's Cornish nursery in Liskeard, known to be in business at the turn of the 19th century.

Right: Flowering Japanese knotweed in summer - its attractive appearance no doubt a factor in its import to Europe

Despite the warnings, in many respects the horse had already bolted and the relentless spread continued both in the natural and built environment, displacing native species, clogging up waterways and causing damage to property.

The damage the plant can cause should not be underestimated, even though the severity may be exaggerated by those with vested interests. As is the case for many other plants, damage to buildings occurs where knotweed is left and allowed to grow unchecked for several years.

Right: Japanese knotweed growing
in and damaging a wall

Left: Japanese knotweed growing through expansion joints in a concrete slab

Left: Japanese knotweed knocking at someone's door

Below: Japanese Knotweed growing through asphalt
at the base of a rainwater downpipe

IDENTIFICATION AND ANATOMY

The plant consists of five separately identifiable parts; all have different functions and contribute to its successful propagation. Japanese knotweed is relatively easy to identify by visual inspection, although an appreciation of its changing appearance above ground throughout the seasons is required.

Left: Japanese knotweed in spring, new leaves unfurling

Above: Knotweed canes in winter

THE RHIZOME AND ROOT SYSTEM

The rhizome system is a network of underground roots and stems ranging from about 50mm in diameter down to 5mm or less. They are covered in a dark brown sheath/bark, with nodules at each growing point.

Tiny hair-like roots grow from the rhizomes. The whole system grows deep into the ground, up to 3m deep in its search for water. It spreads laterally, creating new shoots which over time form into new crowns. The rhizome is an impressive organ, responsible for the plant's amazing survival capabilities.

Japanese knotweed grows from tiny fragments of rhizome

The depth of the rhizome system protects the plant from the extremes of weather, notably from freezing, and also allows the plant to find water, even when near-surface soils are dry. It provides large energy stores to cope with periods when growing conditions are unsuitable, allowing the rhizome to remain dormant in the ground for a very long time, possibly as long as 20 years. Finally, the brittleness of the rhizome and its ability to grow from very small pieces provides an extremely efficient way of reproducing, with new plants being generated from the growing nodes of the rhizome.

THE CROWN

The crown is a thick woody mass of rhizome packed with growth hormone, from where the new stems emerge above ground each spring. Mature crowns can be very large, and are well anchored by the underground rhizomes.

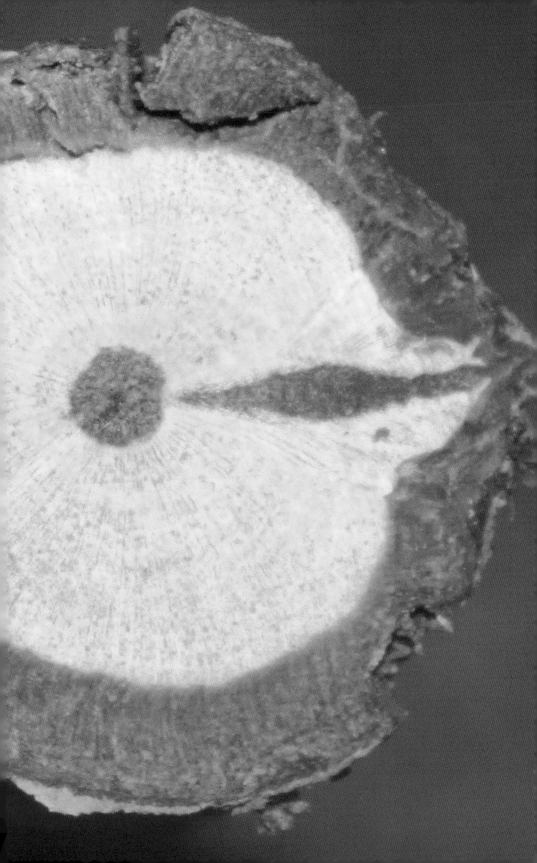

Japanese knotweed rhizome is bright orange internally

THE STEMS

The stems, otherwise called canes, are green with pinkish flecks and originate from the crown of the plant. They are quick growing hollow structures, like bamboo, growing to about 3m in height (4-5m for Giant knotweed). They grow from the crown each spring as red shoots, soon turning green. Shoots from mature crowns resemble asparagus. In autumn the leaves turn yellow and drop when all available nutrients have been diverted from the hollow canes to the rhizome system. The canes then turn brown and become brittle.

The canes are self-supporting structures which elevate the leaf canopy above competing plants to maximise the amount of sunlight the leaves receive.

Right: A close up of a Japanese knotweed cane. Note the reddish/purple flecks, rich in chemical compounds called phenols

Next page: a mature knotweed crown with remains of dead canes from previous years, and new shoots and leaves

THE LEAF AND PETIOLES

The leaf is connected to branches off the stem via a small sub-branch known as the petiole. The petioles grow off the stem branch at intervals of about 300mm on opposing sides to give it its characteristic zig zag pattern. The leaf is the power house of the plant, enabling photosynthesis, the biological process that converts energy from the sun into plant material.

The leaf has a recognisable shape with a pointed tip, known as a "drip-tip". The tip decreases surface tension to encourage water not to "pond" on the leaf ", avoiding undue stress on its supporting stem structure.

THE FLOWER

The flowers are small, clustered and white and grow from the upper leaf axials. They are attractive and fragrant to pollinating insects such as bees. The flower is the plant's sexual reproductive organ. Flowers appear in late summer on mature, healthy knotweed plants.

MISIDENTIFICATION

Several other plants resemble Japanese knotweed, leading to many a false identification.

Even the experts can get it wrong. A label under Siebold's own specimen at Leiden University's "Hortus Botanicus" incorrectly identifies it as "Polygonum sachalinensis", which is the Giant knotweed variety.

BONSAI GROWTH

Regrowth of Japanese knotweed treated with herbicides can look very different to the healthy plant. It tends to grow back with thin straggly stems, small leaves and no flowers seldom reaching heights in excess of 500mm, hence known as bonsai growth.

THE HYBRIDS

Giant knotweed standing taller than Japanese knotweed and with a bigger leaf size.

JAPANESE KNOTWEED PHYSIOLOGY

The plant kingdom creates the building blocks for all life on earth. Like all plants Japanese knotweed derives its energy from the sun by locking together carbon atoms, taken from carbon dioxide (CO_2) in the atmosphere, and hydrogen atoms from water (H_2O), by a biological process called photosynthesis. This process creates organic plant matter, the bi-product being oxygen (O_2), which is released back into the atmosphere.

This organic plant matter, namely sugars and starch, is the fuel that provides the essential energy for cellular activity from a chemical reaction called respiration. Respiration uses oxygen from the surrounding air to break down the sugars and starch formed by photosynthesis, and releases the bi-product carbon dioxide back into the atmosphere.

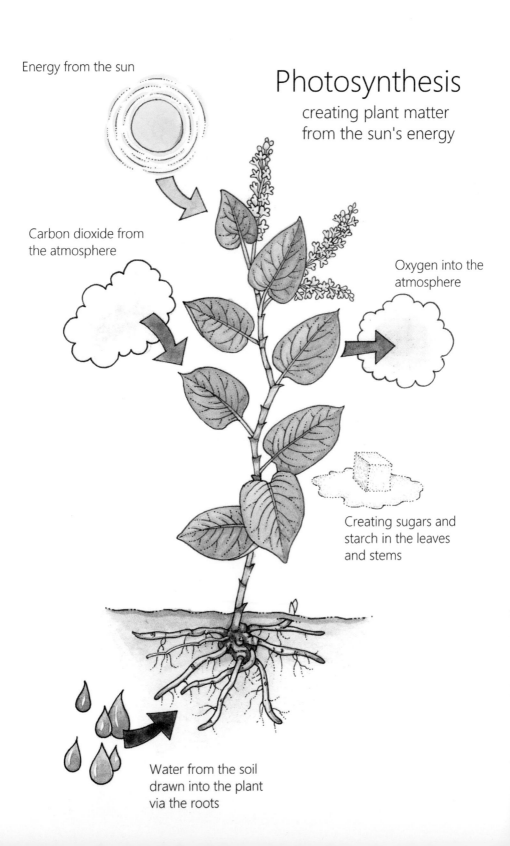

Energy from the sun

Photosynthesis
creating plant matter
from the sun's energy

Carbon dioxide from
the atmosphere

Oxygen into the
atmosphere

Creating sugars and
starch in the leaves
and stems

Water from the soil
drawn into the plant
via the roots

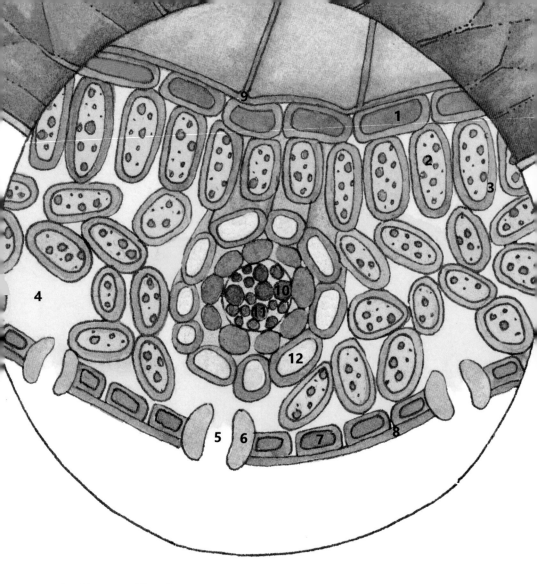

1 - Upper epidermis
2 - Chloroplast
3 - Palisade mesophyll
4 - Spongy palisade
5 - Stoma
6 - Guard cell

7 - Lower epidermis
8 - Lower cuticle
9 - Upper cuticle
10 - Xylem
11 - Phloem
12 - Vascular bundle

CHLOROPLASTS – THE MICRO SOLAR CELLS IN PLANTS

Photosynthetic material is made up of chloroplasts, which give the leaves and stems their green appearance. It is within the chloroplasts where photosynthesis occurs. The leaves have microscopic holes on their underside called stoma. The stoma allows the diffusion of oxygen and carbon dioxide between the plant and the atmosphere, essential to both photosynthesis and respiration.

Transpiration
the water lifeline

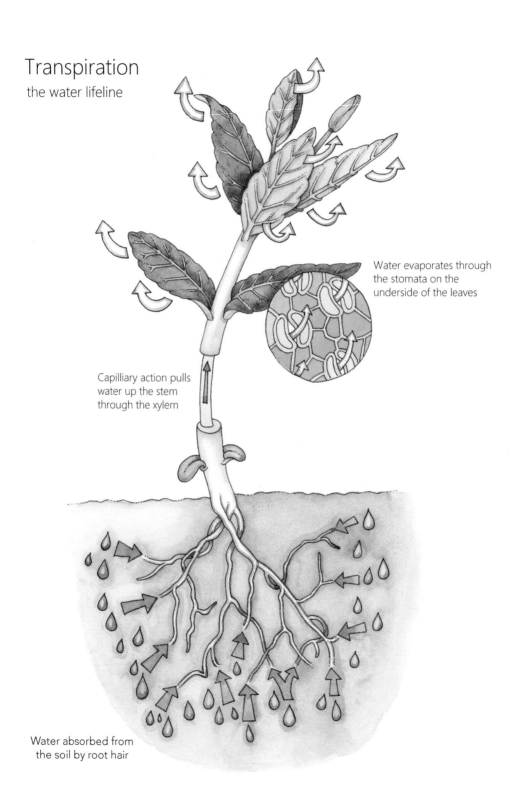

Water evaporates through the stomata on the underside of the leaves

Capilliary action pulls water up the stem through the xylem

Water absorbed from the soil by root hair

TRANSPIRATION

Water evaporates or transpires from the leaves at a rate dependent upon air temperature and humidity. Transpiration causes a suction effect that draws up water from the soil, through the root and rhizome system, up the stems, into the petioles and finally to the leaves. This water is essential for photosynthesis and to distribute essential trace minerals through the plant.

VASCULAR SYSTEM

The rhizomes and stem have a vascular system consisting of xylem and phloem cells. The xylem creates the channel for the upward movement of water from the roots to the leaves by capillary action.

The phloem consists of a series of cells on the outer part of the rhizomes and stem, allowing the sugars created by photosynthesis to travel from the leaves, back down the stem to the growing points in the crown and rhizomes.

GROWTH HORMONES

Plants create chemical messengers or hormones, which send instructions to cells. For example, the most common growth hormone, auxin, when activated, causes cells at the plant's growing points to elongate and divide. These growing points are the stem tips, the root tips, and the nodes on the canes and branches. The hormones dictate when and where growth occurs, triggered by various environmental stimuli. One could consider them to be the chemicals which give the plant intelligence.

There is also evidence that knotweed releases growth-inhibiting bio-chemicals into the soil to reduce competition with other plants in its vicinity. Known as allelopathy, it could explain why knotweed is so invasive in its non-native environment, where native plants have not yet evolved to overcome these growth-inhibiting bio-chemicals.

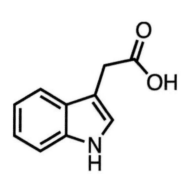

The chemical structure of auxin, a plant hormone that triggers growth.

PLANT REPRODUCTION

Japanese knotweed has two reproductive mechanisms allowing it to reproduce sexually or by vegetative means.

In sexual reproduction pollen from the male plant fertilises the ovules in the flower of the female plant. The pollen is transmitted by insects such as bees which move from the flower of one plant to the next, attracted by its colour, fragrance and the sweetness of the nectar. Once fertilised, a seed is produced containing a mixture of the parents' genetic material, the DNA. The seed is dispersed from the female parent onto the ground, and if growing conditions prevail, it establishes itself as a new plant.

In the UK, and elsewhere beyond its native habitat, Japanese knotweed does not spread by sexual reproduction because there are no male plants. No ovules are fertilised and no seeds are produced.

Japanese knotweed has been known to be fertilised by some closely related plants. However, the seeds have been found to have limited viability and are unlikely to survive.

Vegetative reproduction occurs when a shoot grows from the rhizomes, or stems of a parent plant and establishes itself as an independent plant able to survive without parent plant support.

Japanese knotweed's survival and spread is thanks to its incredible ability to reproduce vegetatively, from very small fragments of rhizome. In the laboratory, under ideal growing conditions, scientists have witnessed growth from fragments of rhizome weighing less than 1g. In the field, fragments as small as a finger-nail weighing around 5g can grow. This, combined with the fact that rhizome is quite brittle, makes disturbance of the ground one of the plant's primary mechanisms for its reproduction and spread.

GENETIC VARIATION

Genetic variation accelerates adaptation and evolution. For instance, in Japanese knotweed's native environment, it reproduces both by sexual and vegetative means. The sexual reproduction therefore creates a greater diversity, making it more likely to adapt and evolve to meet changing environmental conditions than it would in the UK, where the genetic diversity is very small. Japanese knotweed's genetic code is clearly well matched to the UK environment, hence its success. But its lack of diversity could also be its major weakness.

SEASONAL CHANGES

Japanese knotweed and its hybrids are perennials because they lose their leaves and supporting stems in autumn ready for the winter dormancy period, and grow again the following spring. They do this to protect themselves from the extreme climatic conditions of winter in temperate regions.

As days shorten, the incidence of solar radiation decreases, and temperatures fall to a point where the plant can't sustain itself. The water in the leaves and stem would freeze causing irreparable damage. So, in autumn, as a survival measure, it shuts down transferring all the sugars from the above ground part of the plant down into the crowns and rhizome system, and allows its leaves and stem to die. During winter dormancy, its respiration rate drops to "tick-over level", enough to sustain its life critical functions, in order to preserve energy for the following year.

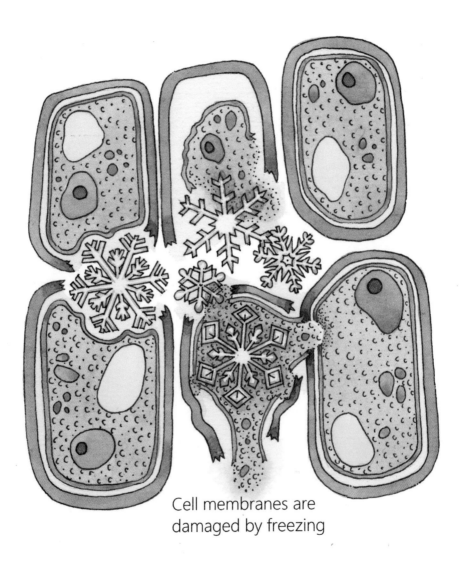

Cell membranes are
damaged by freezing

In spring, the plant sends up shoots from the rhizomes and crowns when it senses conditions are right. This amazing ability is thought to be related to the length of time that the surrounding soil remains above a certain temperature.

The new shoots grow by cell division powered by fuel stored in previous years.

The new shoots at first tend to be red in colour, changing to green within a few days. Once green, the chloroplasts (mini solar cells) become active and the plant starts to photosynthesise again, growing rapidly to build new plant material.

Within weeks, shoots from mature rhizome and crowns take on their asparagus-like appearance.

As the stem grows, more leaves unfurl to create a thick leaf canopy about 3m high. The leaf canopy absorbs all the available sunlight, overshadowing, displacing and out-competing other plants.

PHYSIOLOGY

AND FACTORS

AFFECTING GROWTH

Japanese knotweed is known to grow in many habitats – in some locations it flourishes, in others its spread is less spectacular.

More research needs to be carried out into the environmental factors which affect the growth of Japanese knotweed, but one can get some clues by looking at its native-habitat, and the non-native habitats it has colonised.

The soil and air temperature activates the plant's growth hormone, auxin. This chemical mechanism has evolved to enable the plant to grow in the spring, but to shut down in autumn to protect itself from the cold winter and from freezing.

The soil moisture content is also of importance; it is known that knotweed can tolerate dry conditions for a long period. This is perhaps why the plant has evolved to have a deep–rooted rhizome and root system, as soil at depth retains moisture for longer.

Soil nutrients are important, but knotweed can survive for a long period in nutrient deficient soils. It can also survive in soils contaminated with pollutants such as heavy metals and hydrocarbons.

Soil pH affects cellular plant processes. There is a range of acidity and alkalinity between 3.0 - 8.5 in which Japanese knotweed will prosper; at the extremities of this range and beyond knotweed will struggle and will eventually die.

Soil/water salinity also affects cellular plant processes. Whilst not often found in saline environments, knotweed has been found in many coastal areas and is thought to be partially salt tolerant.

Oxygen concentration in the soil is important for aerobic respiration. This may explain why disturbing knotweed infested soil results in increased regrowth rates.

THE REACTION FROM BANKS, PROFESSIONS AND GOVERNMENT IN THE UK

As a result of the potential damage that knotweed can cause, banks and building societies in the UK introduced strict criteria in their lending policies for properties affected by knotweed around 2010.

In 2012 the Royal Institution of Chartered Surveyors published their information paper on Japanese knotweed. The Law Society was quick to follow with a revision to their standard Pre-Contract Enquiry form (TA6), legally requiring sellers to disclose whether their property was affected by Japanese knotweed.

The UK Government revised their guidance to local authorities to suggest that Community Protection Notices (CPNs), otherwise known as ASBOs could be issued under the Anti-social Behaviour, Crime and Policing Act 2014 to homeowners "growing" knotweed. Legislation originally designed to prevent loutish behaviour is now used to control Japanese knotweed.

ASBOs, banks' policies and the change to the TA6 form had profound effects, attracting a lot of media attention. Awareness of the knotweed problem has since grown, affecting property values, and spawning a whole new niche industry trying to eliminate the plant, estimated to be worth £166 million per annum.

Two trade bodies, the Property Care Association (PCA) and Invasive Non-Native Specialists Association (INNSA) have been established to define standards of varying degree, balancing the requirements of their fee paying members with those of consumers and other stakeholders.

The key to access mortgage lending on knotweed-affected properties lies in the insurance-backed guarantee (IBG). These are issued by the knotweed specialist to cover the beneficiary, typically the home or landowner and mortgagee, for any future treatment of regrowth during the guarantee period, typically five to ten years. Each IBG is underwritten by an insurer, some rated, some not, to cover the guarantee liabilities should the knotweed specialist be unable to perform due to insolvency.

THE LEGAL FRAMEWORK IN THE UK

There's plenty of legislation to excite the lawyers.

Japanese knotweed does not respect property boundaries, and is increasingly the cause of neighbourly disputes leading to litigation where knotweed has been allowed to spread from one property to another. Where a property owner can prove that knotweed has encroached from a neighbour's property a private nuisance claim can be made. Whilst perhaps not in the spirit of the second commandment, it is the last legal means to force an uncooperative neighbour into action.

The seller of a residential property is required to provide answers, in relation to Japanese knotweed, that the buyer can legally rely upon. Misrepresentation claims are surprisingly common and often settled out of court when the seller realises his attempts to conceal knotweed have been rumbled.

Knotweed can be difficult to identify during winter, or if concealed, which is why surveyors should always be on the lookout, particularly those providing valuation services. They are expected to report on knotweed, and those that miss it during their survey run the risk of a professional negligence claim.

Right: Japanese knotweed damaging a wall

SO WHAT IF YOUR LAND IS AFFECTED BY JAPANESE KNOTWEED?

If you own or manage land affected by Japanese knotweed you need to decide if you want to simply control its spread, eradicate or remove it. Leaving it alone is not a wise option, as it will continue to spread – it's a problem that simply won't just go away.

Right: Japanese knotweed growing into a below ground drain and emerging through a vent above ground level

Don't be tempted to tackle it yourself. You'll make it more difficult for the professionals when you finally surrender to it.

You should take advice from a reputable specialist and get estimates for the work. Consider the offering and don't be enticed solely on price. In the knotweed market, John Ruskin's famous quote could not be more apt;

"There is scarcely anything in the world that some man cannot make a little worse, and sell a little more cheaply. The person who buys on price alone is this man's lawful prey."

Make sure that the specialist can provide an insurance backed guarantee (IBG) assignable to a new owner, something you'll need if you decide to sell. Check the small print, you might be surprised at what the policy covers and excludes.

Japanese knotweed in the front garden, an unwelcome sight for any homeowner

A newly laid lawn over knotweed infested soil

Don't be tempted to conceal knotweed. You will need to disclose its presence if you sell. If you give false information during the conveyance of your property you run the risk of a lengthy and expensive misrepresentation claim.

If you allow knotweed to spread from your land, be aware that the adjoining landowner could bring a claim against you. So I advise to do all that is reasonably possible to make sure the knotweed does not spread. DIY treatment is rarely effective and unlikely to provide a decent legal defence if a claim is brought against you. I have seen home owners driven to extraordinary lengths to try to dispose of knotweed. Rolling it in carpet and setting fire to it, soaking it in diesel or bleach or passing an electric current through it will not, I can assure you, eradicate the weed.

Right top: It's best to keep people out of Japanese knotweed infested areas in order to minimise risk of spread

Right bottom: A failed attempt at Japanese knotweed concealment using a fabric membrane and stone chippings

Be aware that herbicide treatment may make the knotweed temporarily dormant rather than kill the root/rhizome system. If this happens, at best you have control, but are likely to experience regrowth for years to come. For this reason, it's never a good idea to build anything over an area that's been previously herbicide-treated. You need to consider having the area dug out by experts, so that no viable rhizome remains in the ground. Some companies remove all the affected soil, with vast quantities being disposed of in landfill sites throughout the country. A far more sensible and economic method is to screen the soil to separate and remove the knotweed rhizome, so that processed soil can be re-used on site. This means there is zero waste to landfill, with less environmental impact, and significant cost savings.

JAPANESE KNOTWEED, THE ROOT OF EVIL OR A VALUABLE PLANT?

The human race has the intelligence and technology to exploit this truly incredible plant. Is it possible to find a valuable use for the so called root of evil?

The following suggestions come with a health warning, do not to try them at home! The plant can cause adverse health effects, and is easily spread. Clearly further research is required, and economic conditions will dictate whether the uses suggested below have commercial value.

Japanese knotweed has been known to contain compounds beneficial for medicine, and has been used in traditional Japanese and Chinese medicine for thousands of years. The rhizome contains compounds used as anti-inflammatories, diuretics, to help digestion, provide relief for a dry cough and to protect aging skin. Ground up knotweed rhizome is known as Hu Zhang.

Resveratrol is a compound found in Japanese knotweed. It has been shown to decrease the viscosity of the blood and act as an anti-coagulant to thin blood. Studies have shown that it can be effective treating cardio-vascular disease, by reducing the prevalence of blood clots. However, in patients taking anti-coagulant blood thinning medication, caution is required to prevent internal haemorrhage. Resveratrol also provides inflammation relief and can be an effective agent in fighting cancers and is sold as a food supplement.

It is also claimed to assist patients with Lyme's Disease, caused by bacteria of the Borrelia type, which is spread by ticks.

Recipes containing the young stem of Japanese knotweed are becoming commonplace and are even being served up in London restaurants.

Due to its remarkable regenerative nature and growth rate, Japanese knotweed could be used more extensively as a fodder crop, the leaves and canes being eaten by animals such as goats.

The above ground canes, once dried, could be used as a biofuel. Because the mass and therefore calorific value of the canes is not high, further processing to form a denser biofuel is necessary to make it commercially viable.

At Environet's R&D facility, rhizomes have been dried, shredded and successfully made into briquettes for burning in biomass heaters or open fires. Briquettes create low-volume high-calorific value fuel.

Charcoal made from Japanese knotweed canes and rhizomes

Japanese knotweed has been proven to bio-accumulate or absorb heavy metals, including copper, zinc and cadmium more effectively than any other flowering plant. Using Japanese knotweed as a soil remediation tool, to remove heavy metals from polluted soils, is a possibility. It would rely upon technology, currently available, to remove the entire knotweed rhizome system, containing the absorbed heavy metals, from the ground.

Japanese knotweed, when processed, can be used in wood/resin composites to make a range of products, for example, in construction and product design.

As the Chinese showed us hundreds of years ago, Japanese knotweed hasn't always been feared and has even been put to effective use. With further research, I believe it could become a valuable raw material for a very wide range of uses. The economic viability and legislative framework will determine whether in the future the plant is farmed on a commercial basis, albeit under strict controls.

I'm confident that Japanese knotweed will one day be considered biological-gold. Keeping it firmly in its vault might be a challenge, but one I'm sure the knotweed remediation industry would cherish.

Global warming is attributed to increasing CO_2 concentrations in the atmosphere from burning fossil fuels such as coal, oil and gas since the start of the Industrial Revolution. Japanese knotweed is very efficient at absorbing CO_2 from the atmosphere and locking the carbon into plant material. If the carbon in the plant material can be encapsulated so it does not decay, then the carbon is captured, preventing its release into the atmosphere. Granted, the effect is likely to be negligible unless carried out on a massive scale!

My R&D team at Environet are working on it - their work might be the basis for the sequel to this book!

ABOUT THE AUTHOR

Nicolas Seal is an environmental scientist and recognised expert in Japanese knotweed and its hybrid varieties. He is the founder of Environet UK Ltd, a company incorporated in 1996 that specialises in providing eco-innovative solutions to those affected by Japanese knotweed.

He is the inventor of Xtract™, comprising equipment and methodology for separating and removing knotweed rhizome from soil, with patents in the UK, USA and Canada.

He heads up R&D at Environet, testing efficacies of alternative treatment and removal methods.

He has made regular media appearances on TV, radio and in national newspapers, and is a speaker at conferences, exhibitions and seminars.

He graduated with a BSc (Hons) in Environmental Science at Kings College London in 1986. He is a Chartered Environmentalist with the Society for the Environment and a full member of the Institute of Environmental Management and Assessment.

He is regularly called upon to act as an expert witness in knotweed disputes and litigation.

'Nic has many years' experience in knotweed management and has produced this book to explain how and why Japanese knotweed has spread so successfully from its native Asian habitats and also to "set the record straight" regarding many of the myths surrounding this remarkable plant. The book is beautifully illustrated with many original drawings by Lizzie Harper and superb photographs. It is designed to be accessible to a wide readership – homeowners especially.

The text follows a logical transition from 'history to identification' then on to some aspects of plant physiology before trying to explain why knotweed has become the scourge of homeowners, how the knotweed management sector has evolved, the different strategies used (with pros and cons) and "What to do if your land is affected by Japanese knotweed". The book finishes with an interesting summary of all the ways in which Japanese knotweed has been put to commercial use over the years (from herbal medicine to food source) and poses the question whether, if knotweed can't be controlled, we should conduct more research to exploit its potential?

In summary Nic's book is part anecdotal, part scientific. It's not a text book for knotweed aficionados but a useful publication for homeowners who want to better understand what this strange plant is and why it's so difficult to get rid of! We liked the layout/presentation and think anyone looking for an introduction to Fallopia japonica will find all they want and need right here!' *Property Care Association (PCA)*